DORIS DORIS DORIS DORIS

DORIS DORIS DORIS DORIS

DORIS DORIS DORIS DORIS

CHOCOLATE®

IS MY LIFE

Featuring Doris the Parakeet   *Ingredients by Doug Marlette*

Published by
Peachtree Publishers, Ltd.
494 Armour Circle, N.E.
Atlanta, GA 30324

Manufactured in the United States of America

10 9 8 7 6 5 4 3 2

Library of Congress Catalog Card Number 87-80966

ISBN 0-934601-31-3

To the extent that the cover and contents of this book reflect the trademark
or trade dress elements of Hershey's milk chocolate bars, Hershey Foods
Corporation has granted permission for their use.

For Joe Radovanic

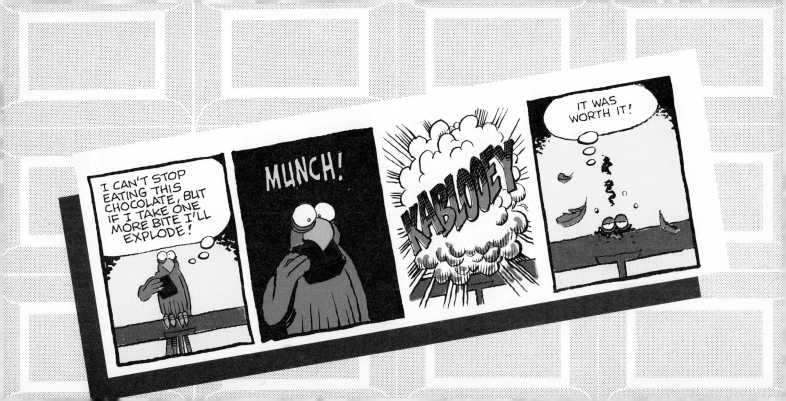

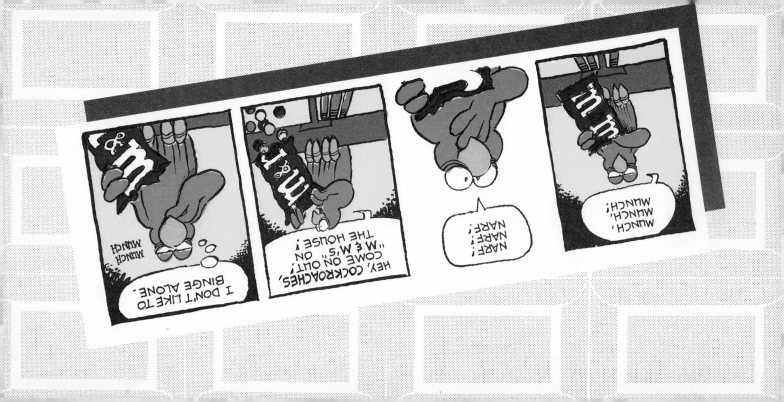

my theory exactly!
IT'S A PROVEN SCIENTIFIC FACT...
..YOU WON'T GAIN WEIGHT...
NARF NARF NARF
..IF NOBODY SEES YOU EATING!...

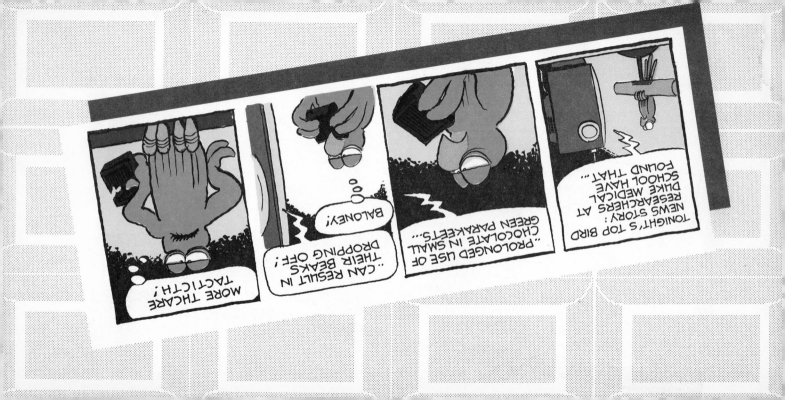

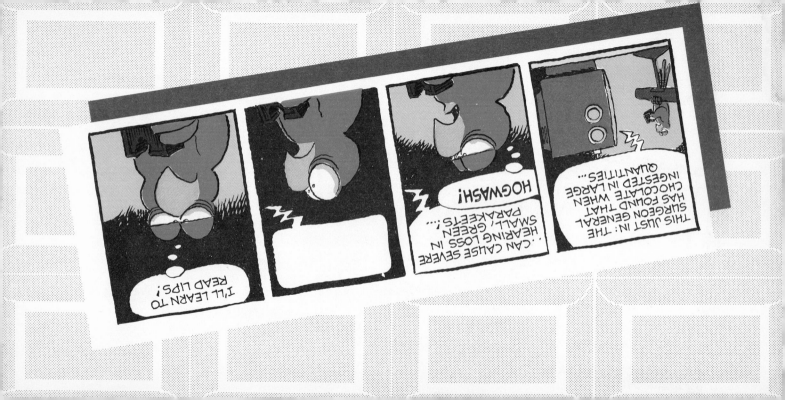

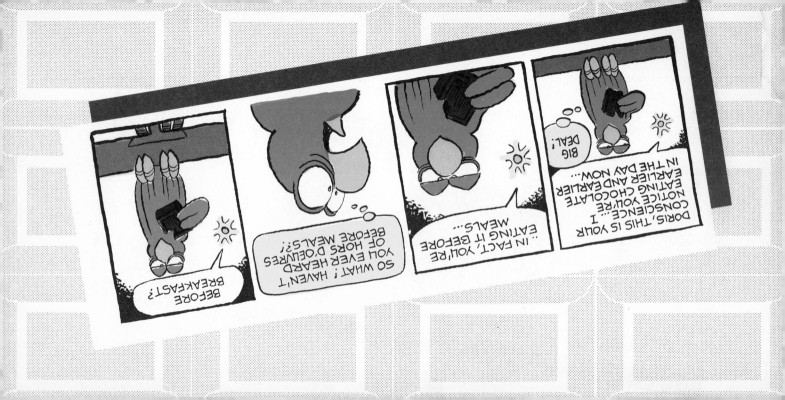

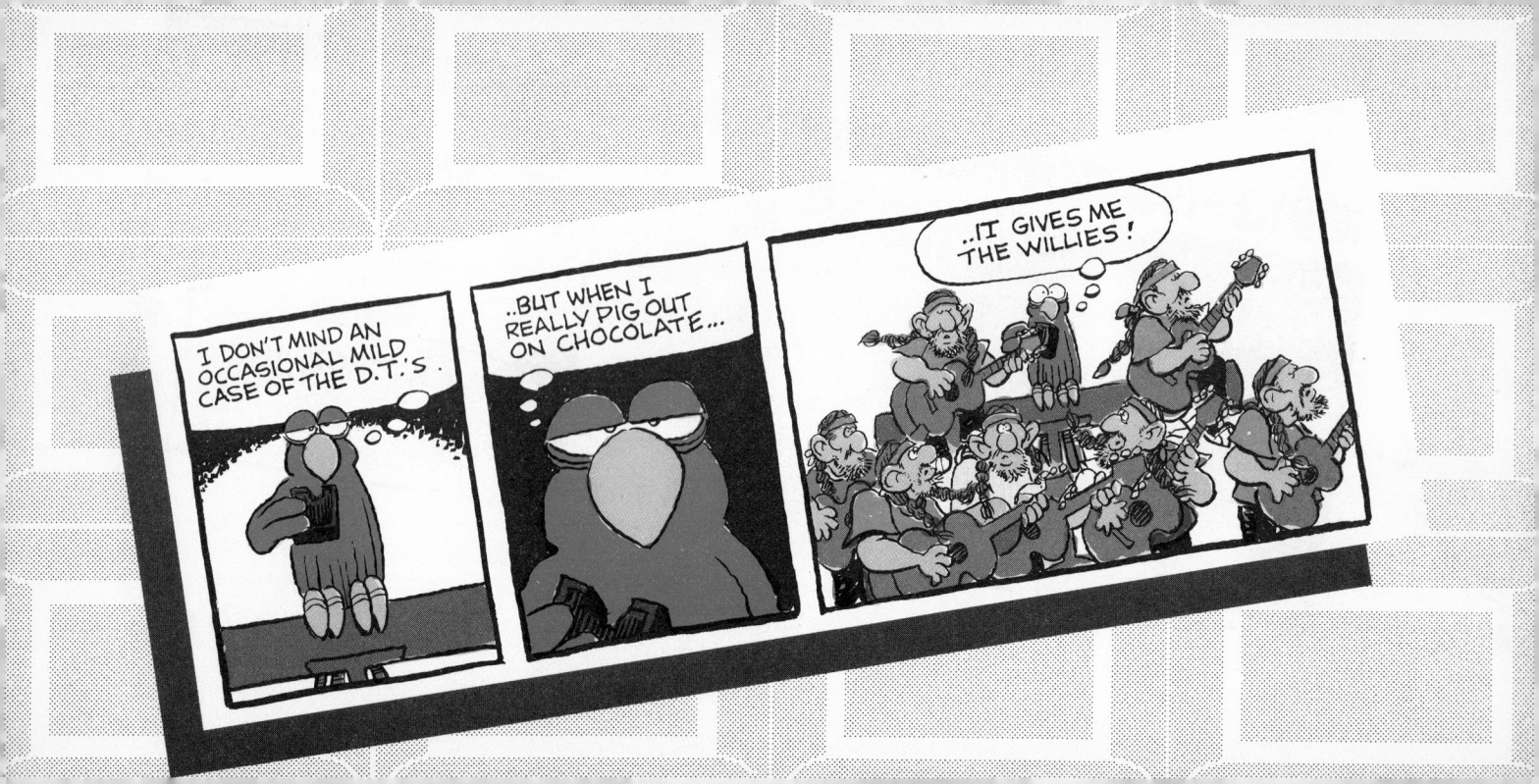

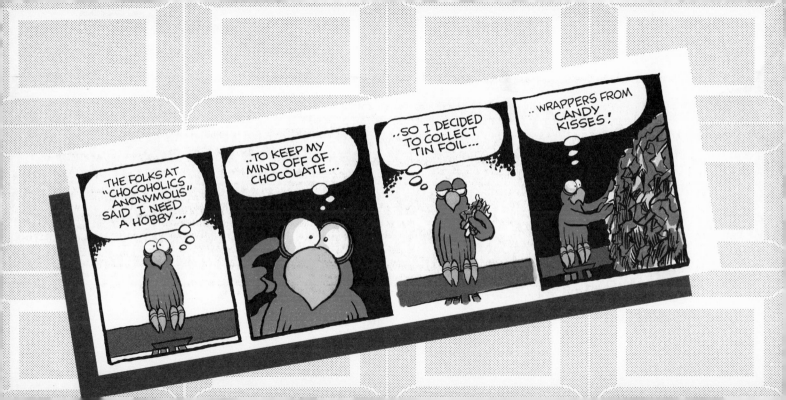

DOUG MARLETTE is the award-winning editorial cartoonist for the Atlanta Constitution. Both his editorial cartoons and his comic strip *KUDZU* are syndicated to hundreds of newspapers internationally by Tribune Media Services. His wife Melinda is a film producer, and they have one son, Jackson.

Doug admits to occasionally sampling fine imported chocolates but denies he once had to have an entire Godiva counter display surgically removed from his stomach.